THE DEATH of GROO

CREATED AND
ILLUSTRATED BY
SERGIO ARAGONÉS

WRITTEN BY
MARK EVANIER

LETTERING BY
STAN SAKAI

COLORING BY
TOM LUTH

**DANIEL CHICHESTER
STEVE BUCCELLATO**
EDITORS

ARCHIE GOODWIN
EDITOR IN CHIEF

OUR HERO

OTHER GRAPHIC NOVELS
FROM MARVEL® & EPIC COMICS ®

DEATH OF CAPTAIN MARVEL • Jim Starlin
ELRIC • Roy Thomas & P. Craig Russell
DREADSTAR • Jim Starlin
THE NEW MUTANTS • Chris Claremont & Bob McLeod
THE X-MEN • Chris Claremont & Brent Anderson
STAR SLAMMERS • Walt Simonson
KILLRAVEN • Don McGregor & P. Craig Russell
SUPER BOXERS • Ron Wilson with John Byrne & Armando Gil
FUTURIANS • Dave Cockrum
HEARTBURST • Rick Veitch
DAZZLER: THE MOVIE • Jim Shooter, Frank Springer & Vince Colletta
THE RAVEN BANNER • Alan Zelenetz & Charles Vess
THE ALLADDIN EFFECT • Jim Shooter, David Michelinie, Greg LaRocque &
Vince Colletta
REVENGE OF THE LIVING MONOLITH • David Michelinie, Marc Silvestri &
Geof Isherwood
THE SENSATIONAL SHE-HULK • John Byrne with Kim DeMulder &
Petra Scotese
CONAN THE BARBARIAN IN THE WITCH QUEEN OF ACHERON • Don Kraar, Gary Kwapisz &
Art Nichols
GREENBERG THE VAMPIRE • J. M. DeMatteis & Mark Badger
MARADA THE SHE-WOLF • Christopher Claremont & John Bolton
THE AMAZING SPIDER-MAN IN HOOKY • Susan K. Putney & Berni Wrightson
INTO SHAMBALLA • J. M. DeMatteis & Dan Green
DAREDEVIL: LOVE & WAR • Frank Miller & Bill Sienkiewicz
DRACULA—A SYMPHONY IN MOONLIGHT & NIGHTMARES • Jon J Muth
THE ALIEN LEGION • Carl Potts, Alan Zelenetz, Frank Cirocco & Terry Austin
EMPEROR DOOM • David Michelinie & Bob Hall
CONAN THE REAVER • Don Kraar & John Severin
THING & HULK IN THE BIG CHANGE • Jim Starlin & Berni Wrightson
A SAILOR'S STORY • Sam Glanzman
WOLFPACK • Larry Hama, Ron Wilson & Kyle Baker
THE MOEBIUS SERIES • Jean "Moebius" Giraud

published by
EPIC COMICS
A New World Company
387 Park Avenue South
New York, NY 10016
ISBN: 0-87135-290-7

2nd Printing

A man named Steed
Went out to weed
His garden and improve it.
He saw a worm
Begin to squirm
And tried to just remove it.

CHOP!

THEY DO NOT KNOW ME-- *IMAGINE!* I SHALL HAVE TO DO SOMETHING TO WIN FAVOR IN THIS TOWN...

EXCUSE ME! WHAT COULD A BODY DO IN THIS TOWN TO WIN FAVOR?

WELL, YOU WOULD BE *VERY* POPULAR IF YOU WERE TO KILL GROO!

THEN THAT IS WHAT I SHALL DO! I SHALL KILL GROO! I SHALL KILL HIM DEAD!

DO YOU HAVE A *SECOND* CHOICE?

HEAR THAT JOKE, SYLVA? THE STRANGER IS COMEDIC!

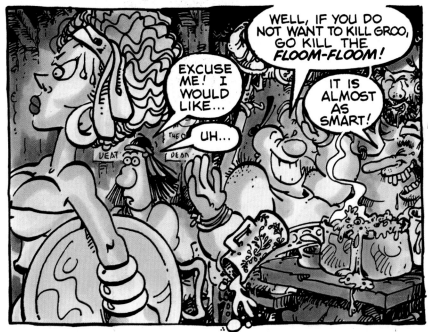

EXCUSE ME! I WOULD LIKE...

UH...

WELL, IF YOU DO NOT WANT TO KILL GROO, GO KILL THE *FLOOM-FLOOM!*

IT IS ALMOST AS SMART!

I SHALL KILL THE *FLOOM-FLOOM!* I KNOW I CAN! IT DOES NOT HAVE A CHANCE! I SHALL KILL THE *FLOOM-FLOOM!*

I WONDER WHAT IT IS...

They had to choose—
Who'd bring the news—
And tell his royal highness—
And so they picked—
A derelict—
Not overcome by shyness...

SIRE--GROO WAS SPOTTED IN TOWN...

"GROO?"

KILL HIM! KILL HIM DEAD! THEN KILL HIM AGAIN AND AGAIN! THEN KILL HIM FOUR MORE TIMES! THEN KEEP KILLING HIM FOR SIX HOURS! THEN DO YOU KNOW WHAT YOU MUST DO?

WHAT, SIRE?

KILL GROO AGAIN!

WE CANNOT, SIRE! WE KNOW HOW YOU WERE SO LOOKING FORWARD TO KILLING GROO BUT THE FLOOM-FLOOM HAS ALREADY DONE SO!

And so the king
Does dance and sing—
With total jubilation!
If it is true,
The death of Groo—
Is cause for celebration!

GROO IS DEAD! HAIL THE FLOOM-FLOOM! HA HA! GROO IS DEAD!

I LOVE IT!

Despite his cheer, he's brought us here—
To where they saw Groo fleeing—
To verify that he did die—
This fact, they're guaranteeing!

NO, GROO HAS NOT COME DOWN FROM THE HILLS... BUT WE HEARD THE FLOOM-FLOOM...

THEN YOU WILL GO UP AND CHECK! TAKE A MAN WITH YOU AND MAKE CERTAIN GROO IS DEAD! I WANT TO SEE THE BODY!

From hills and groves—
They came in droves—
The unknown and the famous—
To hear the priest
Declare deceased—
The wand'ring ignoramous.

The church was packed—
To cheer the fact—
That Groo had met his ending.
They'd eulogize—
His true demise—
With everyone attending!

I have to hide— That deep inside—
I'm one of those Romantics—
But not one bit— Can I admit—
I'll miss his silly antics!

So hear my song— And come along—
The services are starting—

A hefty cast—
Is now amassed—
To glorify the
parting!

THE CHURCH
IS SO
CROWDED...

SO MANY PEOPLE! I HAD
NOT IMAGINED SO MANY WOULD
MOURN MY LOSS!

SCATTER THESE ASHES AT SEA!

GROO IS DEAD...

IT IS FUN JUST TO *THINK* ABOUT IT.

HEY, OLD WOMAN! WE ARE SETTING SAIL! WHAT ARE *YOU* DOING DOWN HERE?

A WOMAN ABOARD A SHIP IS *BAD LUCK!*

I AM NOT A WOMAN! I AM *GROO!*

"GROO?" THAT IS *WORSE* LUCK!

DO NOT GIVE ME AWAY OR I WILL--

I DO NOT HAVE MY SWORDS...

I AM *LOST!*

Sergio by Mark

Mark by Sergio

ARAGONÉS

(given name: SERGIO) is probably the fastest cartoonist in the world. He draws three times as fast as anyone else but, since he puts three times as much drawing on his every page, it all averages out about the same. Señor Aragonés hails from Spain by way of Mexico and has been filling the pages of **MAD** Magazine since 1963, usually drawing in the margins but, occasionally, on the pages, as well.

His highly-original pantomime cartoons have turned up on record album covers, billboards, movie posters, ads and about half the napkins ever used at Canter's Delicatessen. He has also been featured, as cartoonist and/or actor, on TV shows including "The New Laugh-In" and "Speak Up, America." He created **GROO THE WANDERER** in the seventies, got the stupid little fellow into print in the eighties and hopes to see some cash from his efforts before the nineties are up. This is doubtful.

Mark EVANIER

usually gets some silly, ambiguous credit on the monthly issues of **GROO** ("Logolept" probably being the dumbest of these) but is fully culpable as Writer of this Graphic Novel ("Graphic Novel" being a euphemism for the same stuff on better paper at three times the length and seven times the cost). Evanier hails from Los Angeles and, at age thirty-five, has been a Professional Writer every moment since he got out of High School -- which, big deal, was about three weeks ago. His many and varied TV writing jobs have ended countless careers -- where have you seen Gabe Kaplan lately? -- and he was once beaten out for an Emmy Award by Mr. Rogers, somehow poetic. Evanier has written hundreds and hundreds of comic books ranging from Disney Stuff to **Blackhawk** to The **DNAgents** and, most recently, **Crossfire**. His latest achievement, however, is writing silly bios for the back of the Groo Graphic Novel.

Stan by Tom

STAN SAKAI

is way too talented to be wasting his time lettering **GROO** comic books...as any follower of his acclaimed **Usagi Yojimbo** funnybook can easily attest.

Tom Luth

has applied his expert coloring to dozens of comics, every one of which was easier and more profitable for this fine artist than coloring the crazed scribblings of Sergio.

Tom by Stan